THE
Best
IN MOVIE SHEET MUSIC

ARRANGED BY DAN COATES

STAR WARS TRILOGY SPECIAL EDITION LOGO: ®, TM AND © 1997 Lucasfilm Ltd

Project Manager: Carol Cuellar
Cover Design: Frank Milone & Debbie Lipton

© 1997 WARNER BROS. PUBLICATIONS
All Rights Reserved

Dan Coates

One of today's foremost personalities in the field of printed music, Dan Coates has been providing teachers and professional musicians with quality piano material since 1975. Equally adept in arranging for beginners or accomplished musicians, his Big Note, Easy Piano and Professional Touch arrangements have made a significant contribution to the industry.

Born in Syracuse, New York, Dan began to play piano at age four. By the time he was 15, he'd won a New York State competition for music composers. After high school graduation, he toured the United States, Canada and Europe as an arranger and pianist with the world-famous group "Up With People".

Dan settled in Miami, Florida, where he studied piano with Ivan Davis at the University of Miami while playing professionally throughout southern Florida. To date, his performance credits include appearances on "Murphy Brown," "My Sister Sam" and at the Opening Ceremonies of the 1984 Summer Olympics in Los Angeles. Dan has also accompanied such artists as Dusty Springfield and Charlotte Rae.

In 1982, Dan began his association with Warner Bros. Publications - an association which has produced more than 400 Dan Coates books and sheets. Throughout the year he conducts piano workshops nation-wide, during which he demonstrates his popular arrangements.

CONTENTS

FOOLISH GAMES

Words and Music by
JEWEL KILCHER
Arranged by DAN COATES

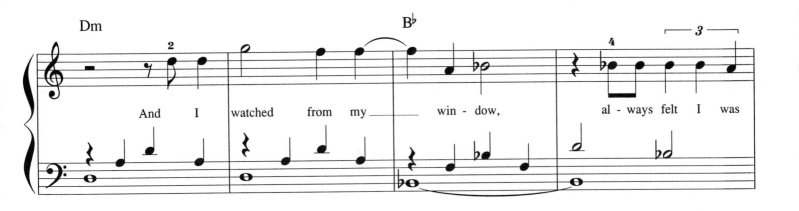

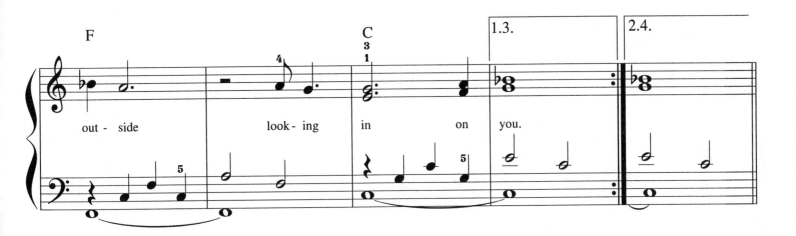

Chorus:

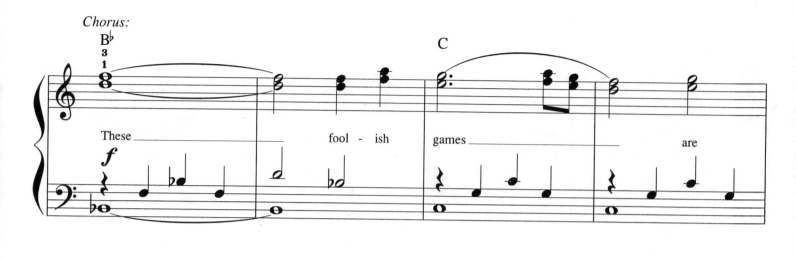

These _____ fool - ish games _____ are

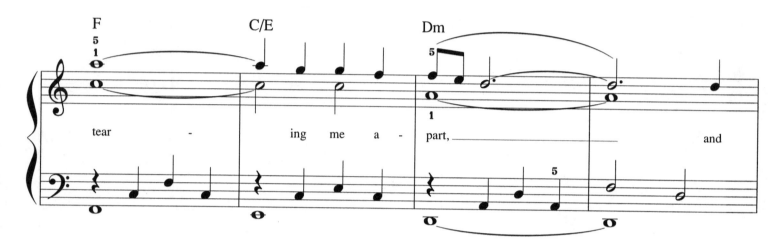

tear - ing me a - part, _____ and

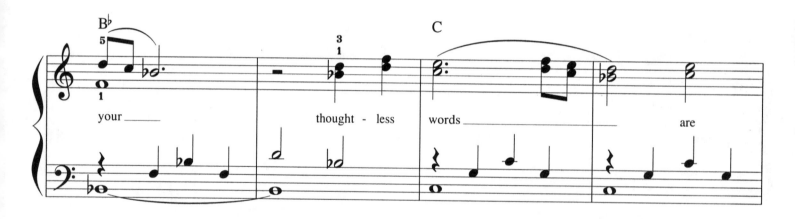

your _____ thought - less words _____ are

break - ing my heart. _____ You're break - ing my

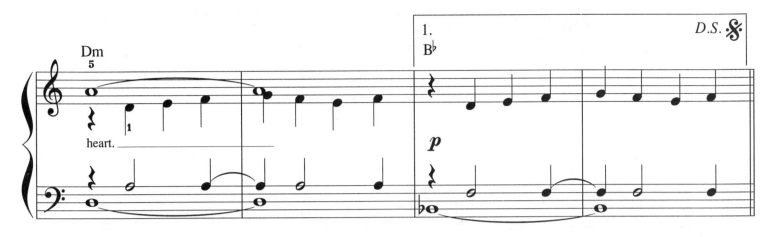

Verse 2:
You're always the mysterious one
With dark eyes and careless hair,
You were fashionably sensitive
But too cool to care.
You stood in my doorway with nothing to say
Besides some comment on the weather.
(To Bridge:)

Verse 3:
You're always brilliant in the morning,
Smoking your cigarettes and talking over coffee.
Your philosophies on art, Baroque moved you.
You loved Mozart and you'd speak of your loved ones
As I clumsily strummed my guitar.

Verse 4:
You'd teach me of honest things,
Things that were daring, things that were clean.
Things that knew what an honest dollar did mean.
I hid my soiled hands behind my back.
Somewhere along the line,
I must have gone off track with you.

Bridge 2:
Excuse me, I think I've mistaken you
For somebody else,
Somebody who gave a damn,
Somebody more like myself.
(To Chorus:)

BECAUSE YOU LOVED ME
(Theme from "Up Close & Personal")

Words and Music by
DIANE WARREN
Arrnaged by DAN COATES

Because You Loved Me - 5 - 1

10

YOU LIGHT UP MY LIFE

Words and Music by
JOE BROOKS
Arranged by DAN COATES

Coda

nights cresc. with song. It can't be wrong when it feels so right, 'cause you, light up my life.

You Light Up My Life - 3 - 3

From the Lucasfilm Ltd. Productions "STAR WARS", "THE EMPIRE STRIKES BACK"
and "RETURN OF THE JEDI" - Twentieth Century-Fox Releases.

STAR WARS
(Main Theme)

Music by
JOHN WILLIAMS
Arranged by DAN COATES

PACHELBEL CANON IN D

By
JOHANN PACHELBEL
Arranged by DAN COATES

Pachelbel Canon in D - 4 - 2

Pachelbel Canon in D - 4 - 4

HOW DO I LIVE

Words and Music by
DIANE WARREN
Arranged by DAN COATES

24

How do I, how do I, oh, how do I live?

2. With - out you

how do I, oh, how do I live?

you ev - er leave,

ba - by, you would take a - way ev - 'ry - thing.

If

Verse 2:
Without you, there'd be no sun in my sky,
There would be no love in my life,
There'd be no world left for me.
And I, baby, I don't know what I would do,
I'd be lost if I lost you.
If you ever leave,
Baby, you would take away everything
Real in my life.
And tell me now...
(To Chorus:)

COLORS OF THE WIND
(From Walt Disney's "POCAHONTAS")

Lyrics by
STEPHEN SCHWARTZ

Music by
ALAN MENKEN
Arranged by DAN COATES

Colors of the Wind - 4 - 1

Color of the Wind - 4 - 2

28

FOR YOU I WILL

Words and Music by
DIANE WARREN
Arranged by DAN COATES

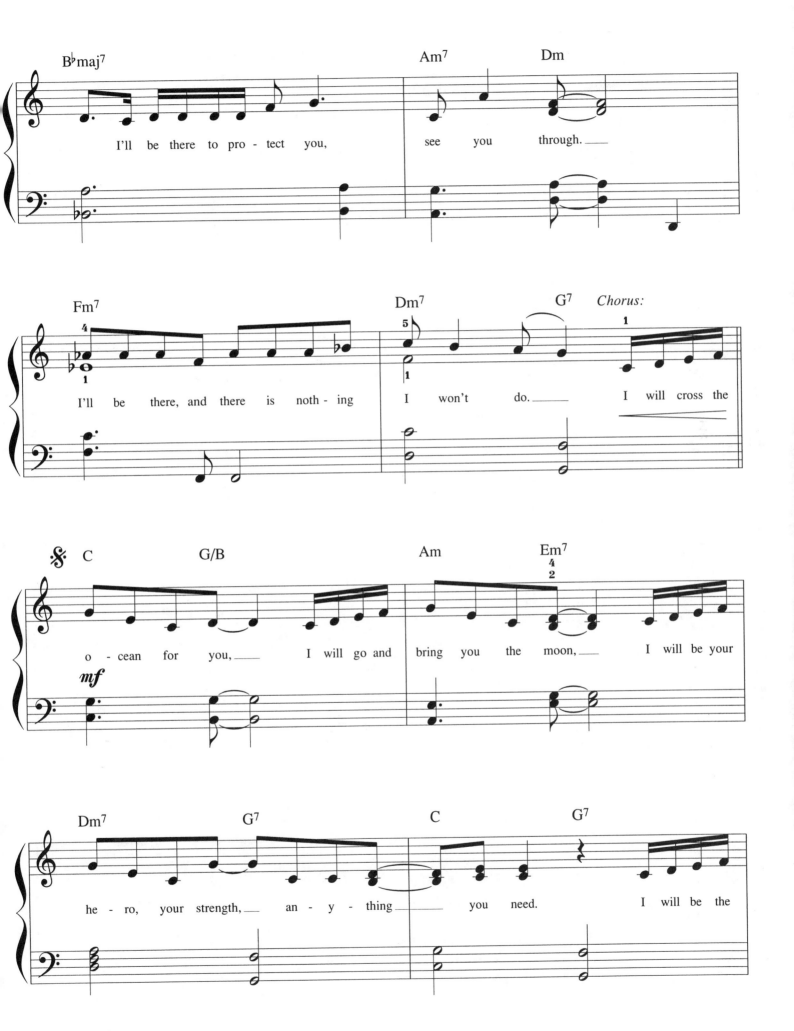

For You I Will - 4 - 2

give my word, I'll give it all. Put your faith in me, I'll do an-y-thing. I will cross the

Coda ⊕

will. Prom - ise you, for you I

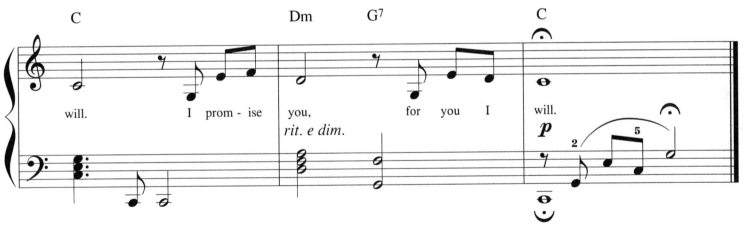

will. I prom - ise you, for you I will.

rit. e dim.

Verse 2:
I will shield your heart from the rain,
I won't let no harm come your way.
Oh, these arms will be your shelter,
No, these arms won't let you down.
If there is a mountain to move,
I will move that mountain for you.
I'm here for you, I'm here forever.
I will be a fortress, tall and strong.
I'll keep you safe, I'll stand beside you,
Right or wrong. *(To Chorus:)*

GOD HELP THE OUTCASTS
(From Walt Disney's "THE HUNCHBACK OF NOTRE DAME")

Lyrics by
STEPHEN SCHWARTZ

Music by
ALAN MENKEN
Arranged by DAN COATES

36

38

ONCE UPON A DREAM
(From Walt Disney's "SLEEPING BEAUTY")

Words and Adaptation of Music by
SAMMY FAIN and JACK LAWRENCE
Arranged by DAN COATES

Moderate waltz tempo

40

Once Upon a Dream - 3 - 2

41

Once Upon a Dream - 3 - 3

I BELIEVE I CAN FLY

Words and Music by
R. KELLY
Arranged by DAN COATES

I Believe I Can Fly - 4 - 1

From the Motion Picture "THE PREACHER'S WIFE"

I BELIEVE IN YOU AND ME

Words and Music by
SANDY LINZER and DAVID WOLFERT
Arranged by DAN COATES

48

Verse 2:
I will never leave your side,
I will never hurt your pride.
When all the chips are down,
I will always be around
Just to be right where you are, my love.
Oh, I love you, boy.
I will never leave you out,
I will always let you in
To places no one has ever been.
Deep inside, can't you see?
I believe in you and me.

From the Motion Picture "THE MIRROR HAS TWO FACES"

I FINALLY FOUND SOMEONE

Written by
BARBRA STREISAND, MARVIN HAMLISCH,
R. J. LANGE and BRYAN ADAMS
Arranged by DAN COATES

54

From the Motion Picture "THE WIZARD OF OZ"

OVER THE RAINBOW

Words by
E.Y. HARBURG

Music by
HAROLD ARLEN
Arranged by DAN COATES

Over the Rainbow - 3 - 1

58

From the Metro-Goldwyn-Mayer Musical Production "SINGIN' IN THE RAIN"

SINGIN' IN THE RAIN

Lyric by
ARTHUR FREED

Music by
NACIO HERB BROWN
Arranged by DAN COATES

Moderate ♩ = 64

mp

mf

I'm sing - in' in the rain, just

sing - in' in the rain. What a glo - ri - ous

feel - ing, I'm hap - py a - gain. I'm

Singin' in the Rain - 3 - 1

60

Singin' in the Rain - 3 - 2

Singin' in the Rain - 3 - 3

62

Theme Song from the Mirisch-G&E Production, "THE PINK PANTHER," a United Artists Release

THE PINK PANTHER

Music by
HENRY MANCINI
Arranged by DAN COATES

The Pink Panther - 2 - 1

From the Broadway Musical Production "A LITTLE NIGHT MUSIC"

SEND IN THE CLOWNS
(From "A Little Night Music")

Music and Lyrics by
STEPHEN SONDHEIM
Arranged by DAN COATES

Send in the Clowns - 4 - 1

Send in the Clowns - 4 - 2

66

Send in the Clowns - 4 - 4

SO THIS IS LOVE
(From Walt Disney's "CINDERELLA")

Words and Music by
MACK DAVID, AL HOFFMAN
and JERRY LIVINGSTON
Arranged by DAN COATES

So This Is Love - 2 - 1

STAIRWAY TO HEAVEN

Words and Music by
JIMMY PAGE and
ROBERT PLANT
Arranged by DAN COATES

Stairway to Heaven - 5 - 1

72

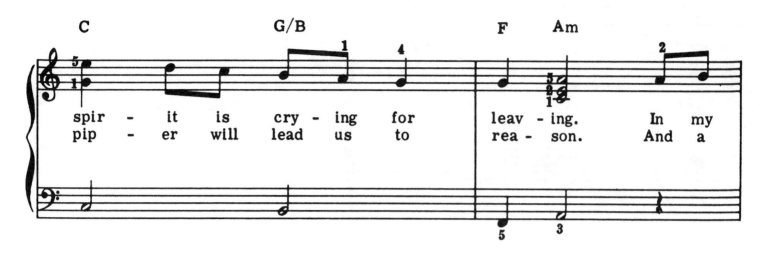

spir - it is cry - ing for leav - ing. In my
pip - er will lead us to rea - son. And a

thoughts I have seen___ rings of smoke through the trees,___ and the
new day will dawn___ for those who stand long,___ and the

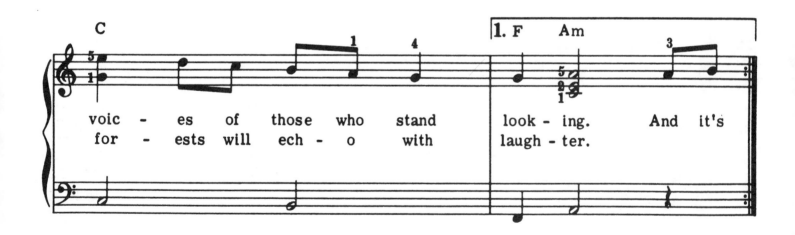

voic - es of those who stand look - ing. And it's
for - ests will ech - o with laugh - ter.

1. F Am

2. F Am   **With a strong beat**
                            C   G/B

laugh - ter.   If there's a bus - tle in your
                            Your head is hum - ming and it

f

From the Columbia Motion Picture "ICE CASTLES"

THEME FROM ICE CASTLES
(Through the Eyes of Love)

Lyrics by
CAROLE BAYER SAGER

Music by
MARVIN HAMLISCH
Arranged by DAN COATES

Slowly, with feeling

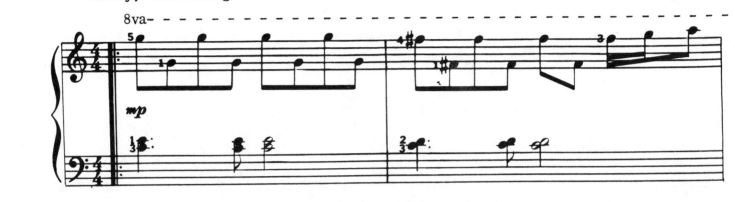

1. Please, don't let this feel - ing now,
   I can take the

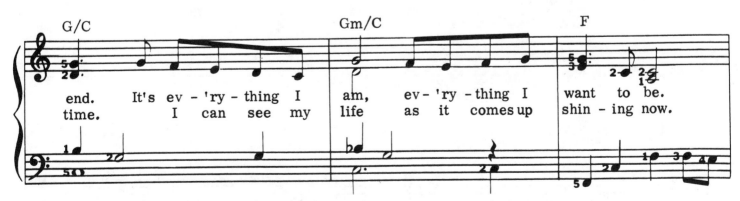

end. It's ev - 'ry - thing I am, ev - 'ry - thing I want to be.
time. I can see my life as it comes up shin - ing now.

Theme from Ice Castles - 3 - 1

76

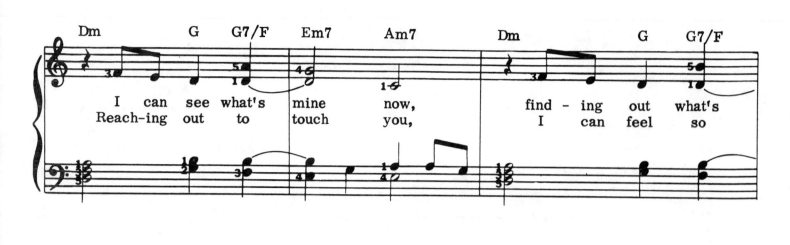

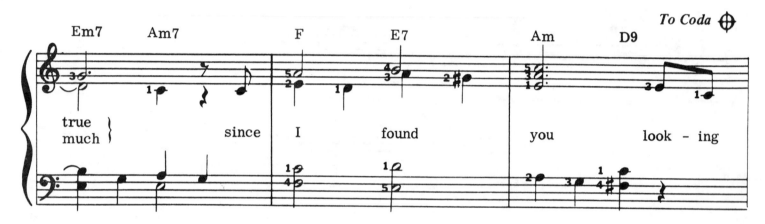

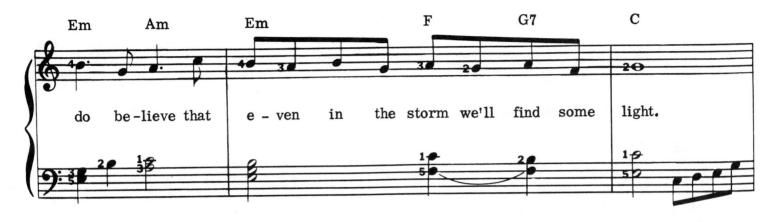

do be-lieve that e-ven in the storm we'll find some light.

Know - ing you're be - side me, I'm all ___ right. ___

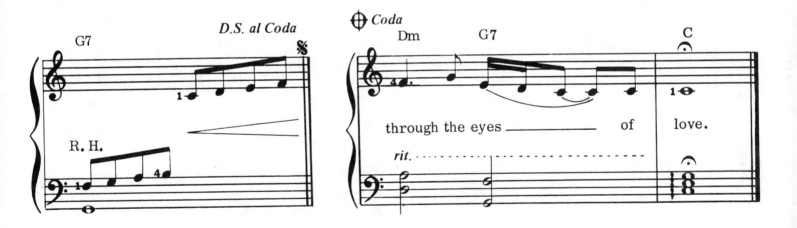

D.S. al Coda

R. H.

Coda

through the eyes ___ of love.

rit. - - - - - - - - - - - - - - - - -

3. Please, don't let this feeling end.
   It might not come again
   And I want to remember
   How it feels to touch you
   How I feel so much
   Since I found you
   Looking through the eyes of love.

Theme from Ice Castles - 3 - 3

A WHOLE NEW WORLD
(From Walt Disney's "ALADDIN")

Words by
TIM RICE

Music by
ALAN MENKEN
Arranged by DAN COATES

A Whole New World - 4 - 2

Verse 3:
Unbelievable sights
indescribable feeling.
Soaring, tumbling, freewheeling
through an endless diamond sky.
(To Chorus:)

A Whole New World - 4 - 4

From the Original Motion Picture Soundtrack "FREE WILLY"

WILL YOU BE THERE
(Theme from "Free Willy")

Written and Composed by
MICHAEL JACKSON
Arranged by DAN COATES

Will You Be There - 4 - 1

From the Motion Picture "ANNIE"

TOMORROW

From The Musical "ANNIE"

Lyric by
MARTIN CHARNIN

Music by
CHARLES STROUSE
Arranged by DAN COATES